About the author

Thomas Hardy was born in 1840
and died in 1928.
He wrote about
the West Country –
the people, their lives and their loves.

iii

About the story

The Western Circuit
was a criminal court
with its own judges and lawyers
that travelled from town to town,
trying cases as it went.

This story begins
with a young lawyer from London,
called Charles Bradford Raye.
He has some business at the court,
and after it is finished in the evening
he goes for a walk in the old town.

He is drawn by the sounds of a fair.

THOMAS HARDY'S

On the Western Circuit

Peter Leigh

Published in association with The Basic Skills Agency

Hodder & Stoughton

A MEMBER OF THE HODDER HEADLINE GROUP

Acknowledgements
Cover: Darren Lock
Illustrations: Jim Eldridge
Photograph of Thomas Hardy © Dorset County Museum

Orders: please contact Bookpoint Ltd, 39 Milton Park, Abingdon, Oxon OX14 4TD. Telephone: (44) 01235 400414, Fax: (44) 01235 400454. Lines are open from 9.00–6.00, Monday to Saturday, with a 24 hour message answering service. Email address: orders@bookpoint.co.uk

British Library Cataloguing in Publication Data
A catalogue record for this title is available from The British Library

ISBN 0 340 74783 8

First published 1999
Impression number 10 9 8 7 6 5 4 3 2
Year   2005 2004 2003 2002 2001 2000 1999

Typeset by Fakenham Photosetting Ltd, Fakenham, Norfolk.
Printed in Great Britain for Hodder & Stoughton Educational, a division of Hodder Headline Plc, 338 Euston Road, London NW1 3BH by Redwood Books Ltd, Trowbridge, Wiltshire.

I

In the centre of the square
was a wonderful roundabout
with lights and music and golden horses.

Charles joined the crowd around it,
and looked at all the pretty girls
on the roundabout.

But then as it went round and round,
his eye was taken with just one.

She was the prettiest, certainly,
in plain country clothes,
but it wasn't just her looks.
Her face was rapt and dreamy,
as if she was unaware of anything
except the graceful rise and fall
of the horses.
For that moment it seemed as if
she did not care about her age,
or her past,
or what she looked like,
much less her troubles.

She looked carried
away, as if in a
dream.

He watched her come round
and round again.
She was lovely to look at,
so young, so fresh,
and as happy as if she was in Paradise.
She was a simple country girl,
but he'd never seen one so fair,
and at each round
she made a deeper and deeper
mark on his feelings.

Then the roundabout stopped,
and the riders sighed
as they got off.

He moved round to where
he thought she would get off,
but she kept her seat –
she had decided
to have another turn.

Charles drew up to the side
of her horse, and asked her
if she had enjoyed her ride.

'O yes!' she said, with dancing eyes.
'I've never felt anything like it
in my life before.'

She was not difficult to talk to.
She was not at all shy –
maybe not shy enough.
She had been brought up in the country,
and this was the first time
she had ever seen a roundabout –
'How can they make
such a wonderful machine?' she said.

She was a servant to Mrs Harnham,
who was looking after her,
but had known her since she was a girl.
She was more of a friend than a servant.
Mrs Harnham was even educating her.
Mrs Harnham was married
to a rich wine-merchant,
but she did not care much about him.
You could see their house
from where they were talking.
She liked the town better than
the country, and she was going to have
a new hat for next Sunday

This is old money.   that cost fifteen shillings and ninepence.

She asked him where he came from,
and he told her London.
He said he liked the country
better than the town,
because in the country
there were girls like her.

Then the roundabout started again,
and he stepped off.

Everything began moving again
round the light-hearted girl,
the figure of the handsome young man,
the market-square with
its lights and crowd,
the houses beyond, and the world at large.
As they spun around her
it was the young man she saw most of all.
He was not like the rest of the crowd.
He had smart clothes and London ways.

Every time she passed him in the crowd
they smiled at each other,
with that unmistakeable look
which means so little at the time,
yet can lead to so much.

When the horses slowed down again,
he asked her if she wanted another ride.
'Hang the expense,' he said, 'I'll pay!'

He says this in a
joking way, showing
off before a pretty
girl.

She laughed till the tears came.
'Why are you laughing?' he said.

'Because you must have plenty of money,
and are only saying that for fun.'

He laughed with her,
gallantly produced his money,
and she whirled off again.

II

The house the girl had spoken of had
several large windows facing the square.

Behind one of these was Edith Harnham.
There was no light in the room,
and she sat looking out,
with her cheek resting on her hand.
She was around thirty years of age,
dark-eyed, thoughtful,
and with sensitive lips.

A man came into the room from behind.

'O, Edith, I didn't see you,' he said.
'Why are you sitting here in the dark?'

'I am looking at the fair,' she replied.

'Oh? Such a nuisance every year!
I wish it could be stopped.'

'I like it.'

'Hmm. There's no accounting for taste.'
He stayed for a moment,
looking out of the window,
and then went out.

In a few minutes Edith rang the bell
for the maid.

'Hasn't Anna come in?' she asked.

'No, ma'am.'

'She ought to be in by this time.
I meant her to go for ten minutes only.'

'Shall I go and look for her, ma'am?'

'No. It is not necessary.
She is a good girl and will come soon.'

But when the maid had gone,
Edith got up, went to her room,
put on her cloak and hat,
and went downstairs,
where she found her husband.

'I want to see the fair,' she said,
'and I am going to look for Anna.
I am responsible for her,
and must see she comes to no harm.
She ought to be indoors.
Will you come with me?'

'Oh, she's all right!
I saw her on one of those
roundabout things,
talking to her young man.
I'll go if you wish,
though I'd rather go
a hundred miles the other way.'

'Then please do so.
I shall come to no harm alone.'

She left the house,
and joined the crowds outside.
She soon found Anna,
still sitting on the roundabout.

As soon as it stopped
she went forward and said severely,
'Anna, how can you be such a wild girl?
You were only to be out for ten minutes.'

Anna looked blank,
but Charles came to her aid.

'Please don't blame her,'
he said politely.
'It's my fault that she has stayed.
She looked so graceful on the horse
that I asked her to go round again.
She has been quite safe.'

'In that case,' said Edith,
'I'll leave her in your hands.'
And she turned to go away.

But that was easier said than done.
Edith was caught by the crowd
and pressed against Charles
without being able to move away.

Their faces were within a few inches
of each other.
His breath fanned her cheek
as well as Anna's.

All they could do was smile,
but neither spoke,
and each just waited.

And then Edith felt a man's hand
clasping her fingers.
From the look on Charles's face
she knew the hand to be his,
but she also knew,
from the position of the girl,
that he thought the hand to be Anna's.

Why she didn't tell him,
she didn't know.

And then, not content
with holding her hand,
he playfully slipped two of his fingers
inside her glove, against her palm.

They stood like this
until the pressure eased,
but several minutes passed
before the crowd had thinned enough
for Edith to get away.

'How did they get to know each other?'
she thought as she walked home.
'Anna is really very forward –
and he is very wicked and nice.'

She was so gently stirred
by the young man's manner and voice,
and by the tenderness of his touch,
that instead of going back in the house,
she hid herself in a dark corner
to watch them.

She could understand
Anna encouraging the young man –
he was so gentlemanly,
so fascinating,
had such beautiful eyes.
The thought that he was several years
younger than her made her sigh.

She watched them leave the fair
and come back towards the house.
Charles was taking Anna home.
Just before they got to the door,
they stood unseen for a while
in the shadow of a wall.
Then they parted –
Anna went on to the house
and Charles returned to the square.

Edith went up to Anna.

'Anna,' she said,
'I've been looking at you.
That young man kissed you, I am sure.'

'Well,' stammered Anna, 'he said –
if I didn't mind –
it would do me no harm –
and – and – him a great deal of good!'

'Ah, I thought so!
And he was a stranger till tonight.'

'Yes, ma'am.'

'But I expect you told him your name
and everything about yourself?'

'He asked me.'

'But he didn't tell you his?'

'Yes, ma'am, he did!'
cried Anna victoriously.
'It is Charles Bradford of London.'

'Well, if he's respectable, of course,
I've nothing against you knowing him.

But I'll have to think about it
if he wants to see you again.
Well, fancy that! A country girl like
you, who has only been here a month,
capturing a young Londoner like him.'

'I didn't capture him.
I didn't do anything!'
said Anna all confused.
When she was indoors and alone
Edith thought how well-bred and gallant
the young man had seemed.
There had been a magic
in the touch of his hand.

She wondered why
he had been attracted to Anna. In fact
she knew as little of men as Anna,
otherwise she would have wondered less.
But Edith Harnham was a lonely and
emotional woman,
and she found herself wishing
that she had married a London man
who knew the secrets of love-making
just as the young man did,
who had mistakenly stroked her hand.

III

Back in London
Charles tried to carry on with his work.

The day after the fair
he had seen Anna again for a walk, and
feeling such an intense desire for her,
he had decided to stay on.
He had stayed for a week,
and had seen her every day,
sometimes twice a day,
and had, in short, won her,
body and soul.

He knew it was a passing fancy
for a pretty country girl,
but she was so trusting
and had put herself
in his hands so completely,
that he hated himself
for playing with her feelings.
He only hoped she would not suffer
on his account.

She had begged him to see her again,
entreated him, wept.

entreated – begged

He had promised that he would do,
and he meant to carry out that promise.
He could not desert her now.

He hadn't given her his full name,
but had left an address
so she could write to him.

But no letter came.

Charles was surprised.
He thought she was bound to write to him.
But there was nothing.

Finally he sent her a brief note,
positively telling her to write to him.

15

A day or two later
a letter arrived at the office,
addressed to him in a neat, female hand.
That was enough –
just for her to write to him.
He didn't really want to read the letter.
He thought it would be full
of silly girl-talk.

Why had he wanted
to receive a letter,
but not cared what it
said?

But when he did so,
he was both surprised and pleased –
it wasn't girlish at all.
It was the most charming letter
he had ever had from a woman.
It was simple, dignified, and ladylike.
He was won over completely.

And so, although he hadn't meant to,
Charles wrote back
and asked her to write back,
He promised he would see her again,
and said how much she meant to him.

IV

When Anna received
Charles's first letter,
she blushed down to her neck.
She turned it over and over in her hand.

'Is it mine?' she said to the postman.

'Why, yes! Can't you see it is?'

'O yes, of course!'
said Anna blushing still more.

When the postman had gone,
she opened the letter,
kissed the pages,
and put them away in her pocket.
Then her eyes filled with tears.

A few minutes later
she took a cup of tea to Edith.

Edith saw the look on her face, and said,
'You seem very unhappy, Anna.
What's the matter?'

'I'm not unhappy. I'm glad, only I –
She stopped, trying to keep down a sob.

'Well?'

'I've got a letter –
and what good is it to me,
if I can't read a word in it!'

'Why, I'll read it, if you want.'

'But this is from somebody –
I don't want anybody to read it
but myself,' said Anna.

'I shall not tell anybody.
Is it from that young man?'

'I think so.'
Anna slowly produced the letter, saying,
'Then will you read to me, ma'am?'

This was Anna's secret.
This was why she was so ashamed.
She couldn't read or write.

She had been brought up in the country,
miles from the nearest school.
No one had bothered about her education.
Since she had lived with Edith,
Edith had started to teach her,
but she was only just beginning,
and meanwhile here was the letter.

Edith's large dark eyes shone
as she read the letter out loud,
though she tried to sound
as flat as possible.

She read it through to the last sentence
which asked Anna to reply.

'Now – you'll do it for me,
won't you, dear mistress?'
said Anna eagerly.
'And you'll do it as well
as ever you can, please?
Because I couldn't bear him to think
I am not able to do it myself.
I should sink into the earth with shame
if he knew that.'

Something in the way Anna spoke
made Edith think.
She asked Anna more about the young man
and what had happencd between them,
and the more Anna spoke,
the more worried Edith became.

She had trusted herself completely to him,
and now, Edith could see,
the young girl's happiness
depended entirely on the young man.

Maybe she should have done more
to stop it earlier.
However, what was done was done,
and now it was up to her,
as Anna's only protector,
to help her as much as she could.
She had to write Anna's reply
to the young man's letter, to try
to keep alive his feelings for her.

And so a tender reply was written
and set down in Edith's hand.
This was the letter
that Charles had received,
and had been so pleased by.
It had been written in Anna's presence,
on Anna's notepaper,
but the life, the spirit, were all Edith's.

'Put your name at least,' she said.
'You can manage that.'

'No, no,' said Anna, shrinking back.
'I should do it so bad.
He'd be ashamed of me,
and never see me again.'

Soon a reply came –
it said it had been such a pleasure
to hear from her
that she must write again,
as often as possible.

And so Anna and Edith
began to write more letters,
each one being penned
and suggested by Edith,
with Anna standing by –
and when the reply came,
it was read by Edith,
again with Anna standing by.

But gradually
the letters became more and more Edith,
and less and less Anna.

Edith had led a lonely life.
She had married, not for love,
but because she thought
it was the right thing to do.
It was a mistake –
and now at the age of thirty
she found herself a woman
She had never been
passionately in love.
whose deeper nature
had never been stirred.

As she wrote more,
she became obsessed with a young man
for whom she was hardly a name.
From the first he had attracted her
by his looks and voice,
and then by his tender touch.
But then with the reading and writing
of such letters,
her feelings had grown.
And her feelings fanned his,

so there was a magnetism between the two
even though she wrote as Anna.

She poured her pent-up passion
into the letters –
she wrote from the depths of her heart,
and he responded to it.

Anna never realised
how much Edith was replacing her.

One morning Anna said
she must see Charles at once.
She begged Edith to write to him.

She seemed very tense.
This did not escape Edith.
She questioned her more,
and Anna suddenly burst
into a flood of tears.
She sank down at Edith's knees,
and confessed –
she was going to have a baby.

Edith immediately wrote to Charles
telling him the news,
and then tried to comfort Anna.

A note came back from Charles
saying he would come down to see her
as soon as possible.

But then a week later,
another note arrived saying that
he could not find time to come after all.

Anna was broken with grief.
Edith told her not to feel bitter
towards Charles,
or to get angry with him.
It was important
to try to keep his interest in her alive.

So she wrote to him, as Anna,
saying he mustn't worry about her,
or put himself out to see her.
She wanted above all else,
not to be a burden to him.
She had written only to tell him,
nothing more,
and he was to forget all about it.

How do you think
Anna is feeling?

Anna's feelings
weren't as generous as this,
but she listened to Edith's advice,
and agreed to the letter.

'All I want,' she said, 'is that *niceness*
you can put so well into your letters,
my dear, dear mistress.
I can't for the life of me
make it up out of my own head,
though I mean it and feel it
exactly the same when you've written it.'

But when the letter was sent,
and Edith was alone,
she broke down and wept.
'I wish his child was mine –
I wish it was!

Why does Edith think
this is wicked?

Yet how can I say such a wicked thing!'

V

When he read the letter,
Charles was deeply moved.
There was no blame for him,
no abuse, just love and devotion.
It made him feel very humble.

'God forgive me!' he said.
'I have been a wicked wretch.
I did not know
she was such a treasure as this!'

He sat down, and began to think deeply.
He was a young man
with a great career in front of him,
but he was also honest and fair.
He really did have a tender love
for Anna, and it had grown tenderer
with every letter.

Finally he wrote back saying
of course he would not desert her –
he could not live without her –
and that he would come down
and solve her growing problem
by marrying her.

When Edith told Anna the news,
she jumped for joy like a little child.

But later when she was alone,
Edith wept.
'She doesn't appreciate him –
how should she?
While I – don't bear his child!'

Edith was now as distressed
as she was infatuated.
He would be ruined,
and it was her fault.
But she could not for Anna's sake
do anything to stop it.

Finally she said to Anna,
'I think we must tell him all –
that I have been doing
your writing for you.
Otherwise he would find out
after you're married,
and it would lead to
anger and bitterness.'

'O, mistress, dear mistress –
please don't tell him now,'
cried Anna in distress.

'If you were to do it,
perhaps he would not marry me,
and what should I do then?
It would be terrible –
what would happen to me!
And I am getting on with my writing, too.
I practise every day,
and though it is so, so hard,
I shall do it well in the end
if I keep trying.

You do it so beautifully,
and say all that I want to say
so much better than I could say it –
please don't leave me in the lurch now!'

'Very well,' replied Edith,
'but I – but I thought
I ought not to go on.'

'Why?'

'Because of its effect on me,'
said Edith truthfully.

'But it *can't* have any!'

'Why not?'

'Because you are married already,'
said Anna simply.

VI

On a muddy morning in March
a cab drew up outside
a Registry Office in London.

Charles got out,
and then helped down Anna
and her friend Edith Harnham.

Charles hardly knew Edith
except for that first meeting,
but during the ceremony
he felt a strange link between them.

Afterwards they went back to his rooms.

Charles and Edith talked and chatted
in a lively and eager way.
Anna said nothing.
She hardly understood
what was being said.

Charles was a little disappointed.

'I think, Mrs Harnham,' he said,
'that my darling is so tired
that she doesn't know
what she is doing or saying.'

He asked Anna to write a note to his
sister, who couldn't come to the wedding.

'Say it in the pretty way
you know so well,' he added.

Anna looked uneasy, but went off
to the writing desk in the other room.

Charles and Edith carried on talking.

After a while Charles got up,
and went to see how Anna was doing.

He found her
still bent over the writing desk,
her eyes full of tears.
He looked at the note.
It was the writing and spelling
of a child of eight.

'Anna,' he said, 'what's this?'

'It only means –
that I can't do any better!'
she answered, through her tears.

'What? Nonsense!'

'I can't,' she said, sobbing miserably,
'I – I – didn't write
those letters, Charles!

I only told *her* what to write!
And not always that!
But I am learning, O so fast,
my dear, dear husband!
And you'll forgive me, won't you,
for not telling you before?'

She slid to her knees,
and held him round the waist
laying her face against him.

He stood for a moment,
then raised her up, turned,
and went back to Edith.

'Do I guess rightly?' he asked.
'*You* were the writer through all this?'

'It was necessary,' said Edith.

'Did she tell you what to write to me?'

'Not every word.'

'In fact, very little?'

'Very little.'

'You wrote most of those letters
from yourself, though in her name?'

'Yes.'

'Perhaps you wrote many of the letters
when you were alone,
without even talking to her?'

'I did.'

He turned away,
and put his head in his hands.

'You have deceived me –
ruined me!' he said.

'O, don't say it!' she cried.
She jumped up,
and put her hand on his shoulder.
'I couldn't bear that!'

'Why did you do it –
why did you?'

'I began out of kindness for her!
How could I do otherwise
than try to save such a simple girl
from misery?
But I admit I carried on
for pleasure to myself.'

Charles looked up.

'Why did it give you pleasure?'

'I must not tell,' she said.

He looked hard at her,
and under his gaze
her lips began to quiver,
and her eyes filled.

'I must go,' she said.
'I must catch the return train.'

But Charles went up to her,
and held her.

'You and I are friends – lovers –
devoted lovers – by letter!'

'Yes, I suppose.'

'More.'

'More?'

'Yes, more!
It is no use blinking that.
Legally I have married her –
God help us both!
In soul and in spirit
I have married you,
and no other woman in the world!'

'Hush!'

'But I will not hush!
Why should you try
to hide the full truth,
when you have already owned up
to half of it?
Yes, it is between you and me
that the bond is –
not between me and her!
Now I'll say no more.
But, O my cruel one,
I think I have one claim on you!'

He drew her close to him,
and bent over her.

blinking – avoiding

'I claim one kiss from you.
If it was made up in those letters,
give me your cheek only.
If you meant what you said,
let it be lips.
It is for the first and last time,
remember!'

She put up her lips,
and he kissed her long.

'You forgive me?'
she said, crying.

'Yes.'

'But you are ruined!'
'What matter!' he said,
shrugging his shoulders.
'It serves me right!'

Edith pulled away,
wiped her eyes,
went into the other room
and said goodbye to Anna.
In three minutes she was in a cab
bound for the station.

She travelled back
in a dull ache of grief,
her lips still tingling from the kiss.

Her husband was at the station
to meet her,
but she did not see him,
and in a daze walked home alone.

She sat in the darkness.

'I have ruined him!' she kept repeating.
'I have ruined him,
because I would not betray her.'

A figure opened the door.

'Ah – who's that? she said.

'Your husband – who should it be?'

'Ah – my husband!
I forgot I had a husband!'

'I missed you at the station,' he said.
'Did you see Anna safely married?
I hope so, because it was time.'

'Yes – Anna is married.'

At the same moment
Charles was sitting at home,
the letters in his hand.
Unfolding them one after another
he read them in silence, and sighed.

Anna was sitting timidly
on the other side of the room.

'What are you doing,
dear Charles?' she said,
and drew nearer to him
as if he were a god.

'Reading over all those sweet letters
to me signed "Anna",'
he replied sadly.